The Far Side®

Millennium

Desk Calendar 2000

Gary Larson

The Ink Group

Originally published in the USA by Andrews McMeel Publishing, an Andrews McMeel Universal company, 4520 Main Street, Kansas City, Missouri 64111.

Web Site: http://www.inkgroup.com

Published and distributed by The Ink Group
Printed in China on recycled paper.
All dates have been obtained from official sources and were correct at time of printing.

AUSTRALIA
The Ink Group Pty Ltd Publishers
111 Burrows Road, Alexandria
NSW 2015 Australia
Telephone: + 61 2 9950 9777
Facsimile: + 61 2 9557 8965

NEW ZEALAND
The Ink Group NZ Limited
Unit B, 8 Piermark Drive, North Harbour
Albany, Auckland, New Zealand
Telephone: + 64 9 415 5529
Facsimile: + 64 9 415 5603

UNITED KINGDOM
Gibson Greetings International Ltd
Gibson House, Hortonwood 30 Telford,
Shropshire TF1 4ET United Kingdom
Telephone: +44 1952 608333
Facsimile: +44 1952 608363

Few periods in history have been spared humiliation at the hands of The Far Side®. Inspired by the approach of a new millennium, we have seized this opportunity to use Gary Larson's ageless wit to impart a little historical knowledge. We gathered fifty-three Far Side cartoons and matched them with facts about often overlooked historical events from the last millennium. The watercolored cartoons and the quirky trivia are arranged chronologically to present an entertaining, if not complete, history of the last thousand years. So laugh, learn, and lay out your days, all with *The Far Side® Millennium Desk Calendar 2000.*

January

Sunday	Monday	Tuesday	Wednesday	Thursday	Friday	Saturday
26	27	28	29	30	31	**1** New Year's Day Kwanzaa ends (USA)
2	3 New Year's Day Holiday (Australia -except NSW, Vic; New Zealand; UK)	4	5	6 Epiphany	7 Ramadan ends	8
9	10 Coming of Age Day (Japan)	11	12	13	14	15
16	17 Martin Luther King Jr's Birthday observed (USA)	18	19	20	21	22
23	24	25	26 Australia Day	27	28	29
30	31					

December 1999

S	M	T	W	T	F	S
28	29	30	1	2	3	4
5	6	7	8	9	10	11
12	13	14	15	16	17	18
19	20	21	22	23	24	25
26	27	28	29	30	31	1

February

S	M	T	W	T	F	S
30	31	1	2	3	4	5
6	7	8	9	10	11	12
13	14	15	16	17	18	19
20	21	22	23	24	25	26
27	28	29	1	2	3	4

Important Dates/Notes

"Everyone can just put down their loot and plunder, and Sven here—yes, old Sven, who was in charge of reading the tide chart—has something to say to us all."

December 1999-January 2000

1003

Vikings begin a three-year visit to the northern continent in the Western Hemisphere. (Indigenous people thought it was going to be only for a couple of weeks.)

Notes

Monday	27

Tuesday	28

Wednesday	29

Thursday	30

Friday	31

Saturday	1

New Year's Day
Kwanzaa ends (USA)

Sunday	2

January

S	M	T	W	T	F	S
26	27	28	29	30	31	1
2	3	4	5	6	7	8
9	10	11	12	13	14	15
16	17	18	19	20	21	22
23 30	24 31	25	26	27	28	29

"You're kidding! ... I was struck twice by lightning too!"

January

1066

What will later be known as Halley's Comet is first observed and recorded by Europeans. In 1910, when the Earth passes through the comet's tail, hundreds of people commit suicide, believing the cosmic event heralded the end of the world. (Apparently, it only heralds the end of those who commit suicide.)

Notes

January

S	M	T	W	T	F	S
26	27	28	29	30	31	1
2	3	4	5	6	7	8
9	10	11	12	13	14	15
16	17	18	19	20	21	22
23 30	24 31	25	26	27	28	29

Monday   3

New Year's Day Holiday
(Australia–except NSW, Vic; New Zealand; UK)

Tuesday   4

Wednesday   5

Thursday   6

Epiphany

Friday   7

Ramadan ends

Saturday   8

Sunday   9

Suddenly, a heated exchange took place between the king and the moat contractor.

January

1078
Construction of the Tower of London begins. In its lifetime it will house a zoo, observatory, mint, prison, royal palace, and is now home of the crown jewels. (It's rumored that both The Gap and Starbucks are currently vying for the space.)

Notes

S	M	T	W	T	F	S
26	27	28	29	30	31	1
2	3	4	5	6	7	8
9	10	11	12	13	14	15
16	17	18	19	20	21	22
23 30	24 31	25	26	27	28	29

January

Monday 10

Coming of Age Day (Japan)
Tuesday 11

Wednesday 12

Thursday 13

Friday 14

Saturday 15

Sunday 16

"This ain't gonna look good on our report, Leroy."

January

1176

*R*abbits are introduced into England as domestic livestock, and they quickly populate the entire British Isles. (Duh.)

Notes

January

S	M	T	W	T	F	S
26	27	28	29	30	31	1
2	3	4	5	6	7	8
9	10	11	12	13	14	15
16	17	18	19	20	21	22
23 30	24 31	25	26	27	28	29

Monday — 17

Martin Luther King Jr's Birthday observed (USA)

Tuesday — 18

Wednesday — 19

Thursday — 20

CLAIRE'S B'DAY

Friday — 21

Saturday — 22

Sunday — 23

"Of course, living in an all-glass house has its disadvantages ...
but you should see the birds smack it."

January

1180

Glass windows appear in private English houses. (Shortly after, the first housekeeper is chronicled as saying, "I don't do windows.")

Notes

Monday   24

Tuesday   25

NICOLA'S B'DAY

Wednesday   26

Australia Day

Thursday   27

Friday   28

LAURE CLAIRE & NICOLA'S 21ST

Saturday   29

RETURN TO SOURCE

Sunday   30

January

S	M	T	W	T	F	S
26	27	28	29	30	31	1
2	3	4	5	6	7	8
9	10	11	12	13	14	15
16	17	18	19	20	21	22
23	24	25	26	27	28	29
30	31					

February

Sunday	Monday	Tuesday	Wednesday	Thursday	Friday	Saturday
30	31	1	2 Groundhog Day	3	4	5 Lunar New Year - Year of the Dragon
6 Waitangi Day (New Zealand)	7	8	9	10	11 National Foundation Day (Japan)	12
13	14 St Valentine's Day	15	16	17	18	19
20	21 Presidents' Day (USA)	22	23	24	25	26
27	28	29	1	2	3	4

January

S	M	T	W	T	F	S
26	27	28	29	30	31	1
2	3	4	5	6	7	8
9	10	11	12	13	14	15
16	17	18	19	20	21	22
23	24	25	26	27	28	29
30	31					

March

S	M	T	W	T	F	S
27	28	29	1	2	3	4
5	6	7	8	9	10	11
12	13	14	15	16	17	18
19	20	21	22	23	24	25
26	27	28	29	30	31	1

Important Dates/Notes

In what was destined to be a short-lived spectacle, a chicken, suspended by a balloon, floated through the Samurai bar's doorway.

January-February

1185

Sixty-year-old Samurai Saito Sanemori, a loyal soldier to the emperor, dyes his hair black before battle so as not to feel inferior to the younger warriors (although, as far as we know, no one has ever said, "Hey, old-timer!" to a Samurai).

Notes

Monday	31

Tuesday	1

Wednesday	2

Groundhog Day

Thursday	3

Friday	4

Saturday	5

Lunar New Year-Year of the Dragon

Sunday	6

Waitangi Day (New Zealand)

February

S	M	T	W	T	F	S
30	31	1	2	3	4	5
6	7	8	9	10	11	12
13	14	15	16	17	18	19
20	21	22	23	24	25	26
27	28	29	1	2	3	4

Rhino recitals

February

1221
The sonnet form develops in
Italian poetry. (Allegedly, it all starts
with "Roses are red ... ")

Notes

February

S	M	T	W	T	F	S
30	31	1	2	3	4	5
6	7	8	9	10	11	12
13	14	15	16	17	18	19
20	21	22	23	24	25	26
27	28	29	1	2	3	4

Monday 7

Tuesday 8

Wednesday 9

Thursday 10

Friday 11

National Foundation Day (Japan)

Saturday 12

READING

Sunday 13

WEEK

February

1252

Instruments of torture are used for the first time by those "fun guys" of the medieval Inquisition.

Notes

R
E
A
D
I
N
G

W
E
E
K

February

S	M	T	W	T	F	S
30	31	1	2	3	4	5
6	7	8	9	10	11	12
13	14	15	16	17	18	19
20	21	22	23	24	25	26
27	28	29	1	2	3	4

Monday 14

St Valentine's Day

Tuesday 15

Wednesday 16

Thursday 17

Friday 18

Saturday 19

Sunday 20

"For crying out loud, Doris. ... You gotta drag that thing
out every time we all get together?"

February

1267
The principles of a camera that can project pictures are first described by Roger Bacon. (Unfortunately, in 1267, film is hard to come by.)

Notes

February

S	M	T	W	T	F	S
30	31	1	2	3	4	5
6	7	8	9	10	11	12
13	14	15	16	17	18	19
20	21	22	23	24	25	26
27	28	29	1	2	3	4

Monday   21

Presidents' Day (USA)
Tuesday   22

Wednesday   23

Thursday   24

Friday   25

Saturday   26

Sunday   27

March

Sunday	Monday	Tuesday	Wednesday	Thursday	Friday	Saturday
27	28	29	1 First Day of Autumn (Southern Hemisphere)	2	3 World Day of Prayer	4
5	6 Eight Hours Day (Australia-Tas) Labor Day (Australia-WA)	7	8 Ash Wednesday International Women's Day	9	10	11
12 First Sunday of Lent	13 Labour Day (Australia-Vic)	14	15	16	17 St Patrick's Day	18
19 St Joseph's Day (Canada)	20 Vernal Equinox (Northern Hemisphere) Canberra Day (Australia-ACT)	21 Purim	22	23	24	25 The Annunciation
26 Daylight Saving ends (Australia-NSW, ACT, Vic, Tas, SA) Summer Time begins (Europe)	27	28	29	30	31	1

February

S	M	T	W	T	F	S
30	31	1	2	3	4	5
6	7	8	9	10	11	12
13	14	15	16	17	18	19
20	21	22	23	24	25	26
27	28	29	1	2	3	4

April

S	M	T	W	T	F	S
26	27	28	29	30	31	1
2	3	4	5	6	7	8
9	10	11	12	13	14	15
16	17	18	19	20	21	22
23 / 30	24	25	26	27	28	29

Important Dates/Notes

"Whoa! This just looks like regular spaghetti! ...
Where's my Earthworms Alfredo?"

February-March

1284

Ravioli is first introduced to Romans, who previously enjoyed mostly fettucini as their primary pasta. (Both, however, come with a side of vegetables.)

Notes

Monday   28

Tuesday   29

Wednesday   1

First Day of Autumn (Southern Hemisphere)
Thursday   2

Friday   3

O.D. DINNER OXFORD World Day of Prayer
Saturday   4

Sunday   5

March

S	M	T	W	T	F	S
27	28	29	1	2	3	4
5	6	7	8	9	10	11
12	13	14	15	16	17	18
19	20	21	22	23	24	25
26	27	28	29	30	31	

"Hey! *You* don't tell *me* what makes 'er tick!
I know what makes 'er tick, sonny boy!"

March

1299
The first mechanical clock
appears in Europe.
(Sundial sales plummet.)

Notes

March

S	M	T	W	T	F	S
27	28	29	1	2	3	4
5	6	7	8	9	10	11
12	13	14	15	16	17	18
19	20	21	22	23	24	25
26	27	28	29	30	31	

Monday — 6

Eight Hours Day (Australia-Tas)
Labour Day (Australia-WA)

Tuesday — 7

Wednesday — 8

Ash Wednesday
International Women's Day

Thursday — 9

Friday — 10

Saturday — 11

Sunday — 12

First Sunday of Lent

"Wait a minute here, Mr. Crumbley. ... Maybe it isn't kidney stones after all."

March

Notes

Monday   13

Labour Day (Australia-Vic)

Tuesday   14

Wednesday   15

Thursday   16

Friday   17

St Patrick's Day

Saturday   18

Sunday   19

St Joseph's Day (Canada)

March

S	M	T	W	T	F	S
27	28	29	1	2	3	4
5	6	7	8	9	10	11
12	13	14	15	16	17	18
19	20	21	22	23	24	25
26	27	28	29	30	31	1

Unknown to most historians, William Tell had an older
and less fortunate son named Warren.

March

1307

Cruel Duke Gessler forces Swiss national hero William Tell to shoot an apple from atop the head of Tell's young son. The reason? William Tell refused to bow to the duke's hat, which was placed on a tall pole in the town's square. (Tell did offer to curtsy, which just made matters worse.)

Notes

March						
S	M	T	W	T	F	S
27	28	29	1	2	3	4
5	6	7	8	9	10	11
12	13	14	15	16	17	18
19	20	21	22	23	24	25
26	27	28	29	30	31	

Monday 20
Vernal Equinox (Northern Hemisphere)
Canberra Day (Australia-ACT)

Tuesday 21
Purim

Wednesday 22

Thursday 23

Friday 24

Saturday 25
The Annunciation

Sunday 26
Daylight Saving ends (Australia-NSW, ACT, Vic, Tas, SA)
Summer Time begins (Europe)

April

Sunday	Monday	Tuesday	Wednesday	Thursday	Friday	Saturday
26	27	28	29	30	31	1 April Fool's Day
2 Mothering Sunday (UK)	3	4	5	6 Islamic New Year	7	8
9 Passion Sunday	10	11	12	13	14	15
16 Palm Sunday	17	18	19	20 First Day of Passover	21 Good Friday	22 Easter Saturday (Australia–except Vic, WA) Easter Eve (Sweden) Earth Day
23 Easter Sunday 30	24 Easter Monday (Australia; New Zealand)	25 Anzac Day (Australia; New Zealand) Liberation Day (Italy)	26	27 Passover ends Independence Day (South Africa)	28 Good Friday (Orthodox)	29 Greenery Day (Japan)

March

S	M	T	W	T	F	S
27	28	29	1	2	3	4
5	6	7	8	9	10	11
12	13	14	15	16	17	18
19	20	21	22	23	24	25
26	27	28	29	30	31	1

May

S	M	T	W	T	F	S
30	1	2	3	4	5	6
7	8	9	10	11	12	13
14	15	16	17	18	19	20
21	22	23	24	25	26	27
28	29	30	31	1	2	3

Important Dates/Notes

Quasimodo ends his day.

March-April

1345

After 182 years of construction, the Gothic-style cathedral of Notre Dame in Paris is completed. (Hipster critics complain, "Goth is so twelve-hundreds!")

Notes

Monday	27

Tuesday	28

Wednesday	29

Thursday	30

Friday	31

Saturday	1

April Fool's Day

April

S	M	T	W	T	F	S
26	27	28	29	30	31	1
2	3	4	5	6	7	8
9	10	11	12	13	14	15
16	17	18	19	20	21	22
23 30	24	25	26	27	28	29

Sunday	2

Daylight Saving begins
(Canada; USA—except Arizona, Hawaii, Indiana)
Mothering Sunday (UK)

"Uh-oh."

April

1348

According to doctors at the University of Paris, the plague is caused by "a triple conjunction of Saturn, Jupiter, and Mars in the 40th degree of Aquarius." (Such medical hypotheses give rise to the advice, "Get a second opinion.")

Notes

April

S	M	T	W	T	F	S
26	27	28	29	30	31	1
2	3	4	5	6	7	8
9	10	11	12	13	14	15
16	17	18	19	20	21	22
23 30	24	25	26	27	28	29

Monday 3

Tuesday 4

Wednesday 5

Thursday 6

Islamic New Year

Friday 7

Saturday 8

Sunday 9

Passion Sunday

Vern waited, hoping to God for one moment—one precious moment—
when the herd would cluster together.

April

1366

King Edward III of England outlaws bowling to keep his troops focused on archery. (Soldiers keep the sport alive by marking down "strike" and "spare" whenever enemies are killed and wounded, respectively.)

Notes

Monday 10

Tuesday 11

Wednesday 12

Thursday 13

Friday 14

Saturday 15

Sunday 16

Palm Sunday

April

S	M	T	W	T	F	S
26	27	28	29	30	31	1
2	3	4	5	6	7	8
9	10	11	12	13	14	15
16	17	18	19	20	21	22
23 30	24	25	26	27	28	29

"Those, sire, are the uncommon folk."

April

Notes

Monday 17

Tuesday 18

Wednesday 19

Thursday 20

First Day of Passover

Friday 21

DAD'S B'DAY   Good Friday

Saturday 22

Easter Saturday (Australia—except Vic, WA)
Easter Eve (Sweden)
Earth Day

Sunday 23

Easter Sunday
St George's Day (England; Canada)

April

S	M	T	W	T	F	S
26	27	28	29	30	31	1
2	3	4	5	6	7	8
9	10	11	12	13	14	15
16	17	18	19	20	21	22
23 / 30	24	25	26	27	28	29

Carmen Miranda's family reunion

April

1418
Because women's headgear is so tall, the Queen of France orders that the doorways of the royal castle at Vincennes be raised to allow ladies to pass through without ducking. (Signs are also posted, indicating a clearance of 8 feet, 4 inches.)

Notes

April

S	M	T	W	T	F	S
26	27	28	29	30	31	1
2	3	4	5	6	7	8
9	10	11	12	13	14	15
16	17	18	19	20	21	22
23 30	24	25	26	27	28	29

Monday 24

Easter Monday (Australia; New Zealand)

Tuesday 25

Anzac Day (Australia; New Zealand)
Liberation Day (Italy)

Wednesday 26

Thursday 27

Passover ends
Independence Day (South Africa)

Friday 28

Good Friday (Orthodox)

Saturday 29

Greenery Day (Japan)

Sunday 30

Easter Sunday (Orthodox)
May Day Eve (Finland)

May

Sunday	Monday	Tuesday	Wednesday	Thursday	Friday	Saturday
30	1 Labour Day (Australia–Qld) May Day (Australia–NT) Bank Holiday (UK)	2	3 Constitution Memorial Day (Japan)	4 People's Holiday (Japan)	5 Children's Day (Japan)	6
7	8 Victory Day (France)	9	10	11	12	13
14 Mother's Day (Australia; USA; Canada)	15 Adelaide Cup Day (Australia –Adelaide only)	16	17	18	19	20 Armed Forces Day (USA)
21	22 Victoria Day (Canada)	23	24	25	26	27
28	29 Memorial Day observed (USA) Spring Bank Holiday (UK)	30 Memorial Day (USA)	31	1	2	3

April

S	M	T	W	T	F	S
26	27	28	29	30	31	1
2	3	4	5	6	7	8
9	10	11	12	13	14	15
16	17	18	19	20	21	22
23 30	24	25	26	27	28	29

June

S	M	T	W	T	F	S
28	29	30	31	1	2	3
4	5	6	7	8	9	10
11	12	13	14	15	16	17
18	19	20	21	22	23	24
25	26	27	28	29	30	1

Important Dates/Notes

May

1420

A pack of wolves roams the streets of Paris, entering the city from the nearby forest. (It was the last time such a thing ever happened and was probably just some kind of animal dare.)

Notes

May

S	M	T	W	T	F	S
30	1	2	3	4	5	6
7	8	9	10	11	12	13
14	15	16	17	18	19	20
21	22	23	24	25	26	27
28	29	30	31	1	2	3

Monday 1
Labour Day (Australia-Qld; France; Switzerland; Sweden)
May Day (Australia-NT; Germany; Finland)
Early May Bank Holiday (UK)

Tuesday 2

Wednesday 3

Constitution Memorial Day (Japan)
Thursday 4

People's Holiday (Japan)
Friday 5

Children's Day (Japan)
Saturday 6

Sunday 7

"Oh, wait! Wait, Cory! ... Add the cereal *first* and *then* the milk!"

May

1472

Vatican librarian Platina's *De Honesta Voluptate* (*Concerning Honest Pleasure and Well-Being*), the first printed cookbook, is published. (Having no competition, it stays on the best-seller lists for a little over a century.)

Notes

May						
S	M	T	W	T	F	S
30	1	2	3	4	5	6
7	8	9	10	11	12	13
14	15	16	17	18	19	20
21	22	23	24	25	26	27
28	29	30	31			

Monday   8

Victory Day (France)
Tuesday   9

Wednesday   10

Thursday   11

Friday   12

Saturday   13

Sunday   14

Mother's Day (Australia; USA; Canada)

May

1477

lad Tepes, better known as Dracula, is ambushed and killed outside of Bucharest. Weapons are rumored to be wooden stakes and silver crucifixes. (His real name is eventually forgotten, mostly because no one is really scared by stories such as "The Return of Vlad.")

Notes

_____

_____

_____

_____

_____

_____

_____

_____

_____

May

S	M	T	W	T	F	S
30	1	2	3	4	5	6
7	8	9	10	11	12	13
14	15	16	17	18	19	20
21	22	23	24	25	26	27
28	29	30	31	1	2	3

Monday 15

Adelaide Cup Day (Australia-Adelaide only)

Tuesday 16

Wednesday 17

Thursday 18

Friday 19

Saturday 20

Armed Forces Day (USA)

Sunday 21

"Did you detect something a little ominous
in the way they said, 'See you later'?"

May

1492

On Christmas Eve, the *Santa Maria*, piloted by a cabin boy, wrecks on the north coast of Hispaniola. Columbus takes control of the *Nina* and outraces the *Pinta* to be the first to arrive home with news of the New World. (The cabin boy is demoted to restroom boy.)

Notes

Monday	22
	Victoria Day (Canada)
Tuesday	23
Wednesday	24
Thursday	25
Friday	26
Saturday	27
Sunday	28

May

S	M	T	W	T	F	S
30	1	2	3	4	5	6
7	8	9	10	11	12	13
14	15	16	17	18	19	20
21	22	23	24	25	26	27
28	29	30	31	1	2	3

June

Sunday	Monday	Tuesday	Wednesday	Thursday	Friday	Saturday
28	29	30	31	1 First Day of Winter (Southern Hemisphere) Ascension Day (Canada; Germany)	2	3
4	5 Foundation Day (Australia-WA) Queen's Birthday (New Zealand)	6	7	8	9 Pentecost Shavuot begins	10 Shavuot ends
11 Whitsunday (Canada; Germany; Sweden; Finland)	12 Queen's Birthday (Australia-except WA) Whitmonday (Germany; Sweden)	13	14 Flag Day (USA)	15	16	17
18 Trinity Sunday Father's Day (UK; Ireland; Canada; USA)	19	20	21 Summer Solstice (Northern Hemisphere)	22 Corpus Christi (Germany; Canada)	23 Midsummer's Eve (Sweden; Finland)	24 St-Jean-Baptiste Day (Canada) Midsummer Day (Sweden; Finland)
25	26	27	28	29	30 Sacred Heart of Jesus (Canada)	1

May

S	M	T	W	T	F	S
30	1	2	3	4	5	6
7	8	9	10	11	12	13
14	15	16	17	18	19	20
21	22	23	24	25	26	27
28	29	30	31	1	2	3

July

S	M	T	W	T	F	S
25	26	27	28	29	30	1
2	3	4	5	6	7	8
9	10	11	12	13	14	15
16	17	18	19	20	21	22
23	24	25	26	27	28	29
30	31					

Important Dates/Notes

May-June

1503

Leonardo da Vinci completes the *Mona Lisa.* Though considered to be the most valuable painting in the world today, it is disliked at the time by Mona Lisa Gheradini's husband, who refuses to pay for the work. (He thinks the smile looks faked.)

Notes

June

S	M	T	W	T	F	S
28	29	30	31	1	2	3
4	5	6	7	8	9	10
11	12	13	14	15	16	17
18	19	20	21	22	23	24
25	26	27	28	29	30	1

Monday 29

Memorial Day observed (USA)
Spring Bank Holiday (UK)

Tuesday 30

Memorial Day (USA)

Wednesday 31

Thursday 1

First Day of Winter (Southern Hemisphere)
Ascension Day (Canada; Germany; Sweden; Finland)

Friday 2

Saturday 3

Sunday 4

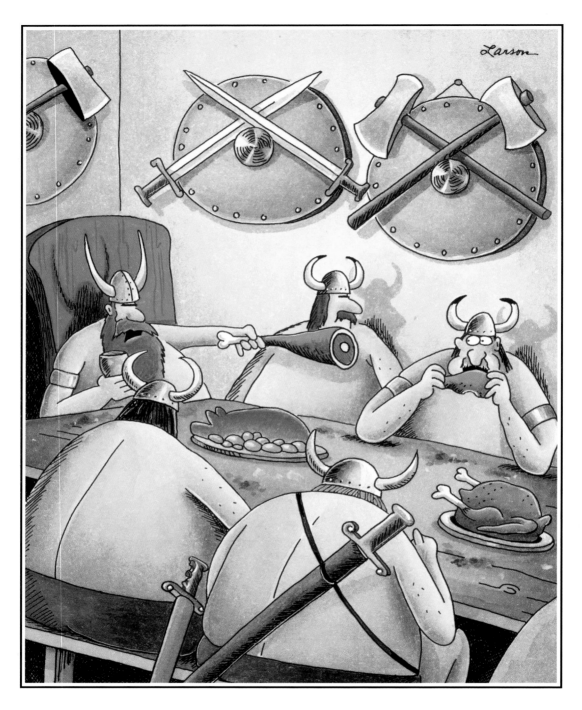

"Uh-uh-uh-uh-uh. ... Question. Can anyone here tell me what
Hanson there is doing wrong with his elbows?"

June

1530
Erasmus of Rotterdam writes *On Civility in Children*, advising, among other things, "If you cannot swallow a piece of food, turn around discreetly and throw it somewhere."

Notes

June

S	M	T	W	T	F	S
28	29	30	31	1	2	3
4	5	6	7	8	9	10
11	12	13	14	15	16	17
18	19	20	21	22	23	24
25	26	27	28	29	30	

Monday 5

Foundation Day (Australia–WA)
Queen's Birthday (New Zealand)

Tuesday 6

Wednesday 7

Thursday 8

Friday 9

Pentecost
Shavuot begins

Saturday 10

Shavuot ends

Sunday 11

Whitsunday (Canada; Germany; Sweden; Finland)

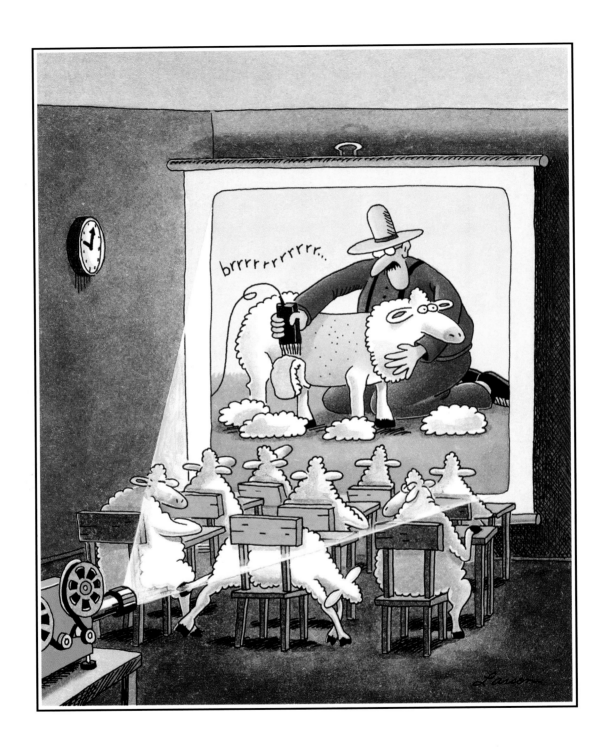

Sheep health classes

June

1541

Wool is introduced to America when the Spaniard Coronado brings several of his favorite sheep to southwestern North America. (Why Coronado found a need to travel by sea with "several of his favorite sheep" is still a mystery.)

Notes

June

S	M	T	W	T	F	S
28	29	30	31	1	2	3
4	5	6	7	8	9	10
11	12	13	14	15	16	17
18	19	20	21	22	23	24
25	26	27	28	29	30	1

Monday 12

Queen's Birthday (Australia–except WA)
Whitmonday (Germany; Sweden)

Tuesday 13

Wednesday 14

Flag Day (USA)

Thursday 15

Friday 16

Saturday 17

Sunday 18

Trinity Sunday
Father's Day (UK; Ireland; Canada; USA)

"Hey! I got one! I got one!"

June

Notes

June						
S	M	T	W	T	F	S
28	29	30	31	1	2	3
4	5	6	7	8	9	10
11	12	13	14	15	16	17
18	19	20	21	22	23	24
25	26	27	28	29	30	1

Monday 19

Tuesday 20

Wednesday 21

Summer Solstice (Northern Hemisphere)
Thursday 22

Corpus Christi (Germany; Canada)
Friday 23

Midsummer's Eve (Sweden; Finland)
Saturday 24

St-Jean-Baptiste Day (Canada)
Midsummer Day (Sweden; Finland)
Sunday 25

July

Sunday	Monday	Tuesday	Wednesday	Thursday	Friday	Saturday
25	26	27	28	29	30	**1** Canada Day **HKSAR** **Establishment Day** (Hong Kong)
2	3	4 Independence Day (USA)	5	6	7	8
9 Khao Phansa Day -Buddhist Lent (Thailand)	10	11	12 Battle of the Boyne (Northern Ireland)	13	14 Bastille Day (France)	15
16	17	18	19	20 Marine Day (Japan)	21	22
23	24	25	26	27	28	29
30	31					

June

S	M	T	W	T	F	S
28	29	30	31	1	2	3
4	5	6	7	8	9	10
11	12	13	14	15	16	17
18	19	20	21	22	23	24
25	26	27	28	29	30	1

August

S	M	T	W	T	F	S
30	31	1	2	3	4	5
6	7	8	9	10	11	12
13	14	15	16	17	18	19
20	21	22	23	24	25	26
27	28	29	30	31	1	2

Important Dates/Notes

June-July

Notes

July

S	M	T	W	T	F	S
25	26	27	28	29	30	1
2	3	4	5	6	7	8
9	10	11	12	13	14	15
16	17	18	19	20	21	22
23	24	25	26	27	28	29
30	31					

Monday   26

Tuesday   27

Wednesday   28

Thursday   29

Friday   30

Sacred Heart of Jesus (Canada)

Saturday   1

Canada Day
HKSAR Establishment Day (Hong Kong)

Sunday   2

July

1590
Dutch optician Zacharias Janssen invents the compound microscope, discovering that it's a small world after all.

Notes

Monday   3

Tuesday   4

Independence Day (USA)

Wednesday   5

Thursday   6

Friday   7

Saturday   8

Sunday   9

Khao Phansa Day–Buddhist Lent (Thailand)

July

S	M	T	W	T	F	S
25	26	27	28	29	30	1
2	3	4	5	6	7	8
9	10	11	12	13	14	15
16	17	18	19	20	21	22
23	24	25	26	27	28	29
30	31					

"I tell ya, Ben—no matter who wins this thing,
Boot Hill ain't ever gonna be the same."

July

Monday 10

Tuesday 11

Notes

Wednesday 12

Battle of the Boyne (Northern Ireland)

Thursday 13

Friday 14

Bastille Day (France)

Saturday 15

July						
S	M	T	W	T	F	S
25	26	27	28	29	30	1
2	3	4	5	6	7	8
9	10	11	12	13	14	15
16	17	18	19	20	21	22
23 30	24 31	25	26	27	28	29

Sunday 16

Hot off the press, the very first edition of the *Desert Island Times*
caused the newspaper to quickly fold.

July

1605

The world's first newspaper begins publication in Antwerp. (Parakeets start to become popular.)

Monday   17

Tuesday   18

MY B'DAY

Wednesday   19

Thursday   20

Marine Day (Japan)

Friday   21

Saturday   22

Sunday   23

Notes

July

S	M	T	W	T	F	S
25	26	27	28	29	30	1
2	3	4	5	6	7	8
9	10	11	12	13	14	15
16	17	18	19	20	21	22
23 30	24 31	25	26	27	28	29

July

1610

Galileo improves the refractive telescope. His planetary theories fly in the face of religious dogma and he is forced to retract before the Inquisition. Nevertheless, he is imprisoned, and the validity of his scientific work is not formally recognized by the Roman Catholic Church until 1993. (Apparently, the Church wanted to make really, really sure Galileo knew what he was talking about.)

Notes

July

S	M	T	W	T	F	S
25	26	27	28	29	30	1
2	3	4	5	6	7	8
9	10	11	12	13	14	15
16	17	18	19	20	21	22
23 / 30	24 / 31	25	26	27	28	29

Monday 24

Tuesday 25

Wednesday 26

Thursday 27

Friday 28

Saturday 29

Sunday 30

August

Sunday	Monday	Tuesday	Wednesday	Thursday	Friday	Saturday
30	31	1 Swiss National Day Horses' Birthday	2	3	4	5
6	7 Bank Holiday (Australia-NSW, ACT) Summer Bank Holiday (Scotland)	8	9	10	11	12
13	14	15 Assumption (France; Canada; Italy) Dormition of Our Lady (Greek Orthodox Church)	16	17	18	19
20	21	22	23	24	25	26
27 Daylight Saving begins (Australia-NSW)	28 Summer Bank Holiday (UK-except Scotland)	29	30	31	1	2

July

S	M	T	W	T	F	S
25	26	27	28	29	30	1
2	3	4	5	6	7	8
9	10	11	12	13	14	15
16	17	18	19	20	21	22
23	24	25	26	27	28	29
30	31					

September

S	M	T	W	T	F	S
27	28	29	30	31	1	2
3	4	5	6	7	8	9
10	11	12	13	14	15	16
17	18	19	20	21	22	23
24	25	26	27	28	29	30

Important Dates/Notes

July-August

1619
The story of the "Three Little Pigs" is introduced into English folklore.

Notes

August

S	M	T	W	T	F	S
30	31	1	2	3	4	5
6	7	8	9	10	11	12
13	14	15	16	17	18	19
20	21	22	23	24	25	26
27	28	29	30	31	1	2

Monday 31

Tuesday 1

Swiss National Day
Horses' Birthday

Wednesday 2

Thursday 3

Friday 4

Saturday 5

Sunday 6

New York 1626: Chief of the Manhattan Indians
addresses his tribe for the last time.

August

1626
The Dutch buy Manhattan.

SOLD
MANHATTAN

Notes

August

S	M	T	W	T	F	S
30	31	1	2	3	4	5
6	7	8	9	10	11	12
13	14	15	16	17	18	19
20	21	22	23	24	25	26
27	28	29	30	31	1	2

Monday 7
Bank Holiday (Australia-NSW, ACT)
Picnic Day (Australia-NT)
Summer Bank Holiday (Scotland)

Tuesday 8

Wednesday 9

Thursday 10

Friday 11

Saturday 12

Sunday 13

MUM's B'DAY

"Latte, Jed?"

August

Notes

August

S	M	T	W	T	F	S
30	31	1	2	3	4	5
6	7	8	9	10	11	12
13	14	15	16	17	18	19
20	21	22	23	24	25	26
27	28	29	30	31	1	2

Monday 14

Tuesday 15

Assumption (France; Canada; Italy)
Dormition of Our Lady (Greek Orthodox Church)

Wednesday 16

Thursday 17

SALLY'S B'DAY

Friday 18

Saturday 19

Sunday 20

In the animal self-help section

August

1704
The first library from which the public can check out books opens in Berlin. (A month after it opens, the first late fee is issued to one Wolfgang Muller.)

Notes

August

S	M	T	W	T	F	S
30	31	1	2	3	4	5
6	7	8	9	10	11	12
13	14	15	16	17	18	19
20	21	22	23	24	25	26
27	28	29	30	31	1	2

Monday 21

Tuesday 22

Wednesday 23

Thursday 24

Friday 25

Saturday 26

Sunday 27

Daylight Saving begins
(Australia-NSW)

September

Sunday	Monday	Tuesday	Wednesday	Thursday	Friday	Saturday
27	28	29	30	31	1 First Day of Spring (Southern Hemisphere)	2
3 Father's Day (Australia; New Zealand)	4 Labor Day (USA; Canada)	5	6	7	8	9
10	11	12	13	14	15 Respect for the Aged Day (Japan)	16
17	18	19	20	21	22	23 Autumnal Equinox (Northern Hemisphere)
24	25	26	27	28	29 St Michael's Day (Canada)	30 Rosh Hashanah

August

S	M	T	W	T	F	S
30	31	1	2	3	4	5
6	7	8	9	10	11	12
13	14	15	16	17	18	19
20	21	22	23	24	25	26
27	28	29	30	31	1	2

October

S	M	T	W	T	F	S
1	2	3	4	5	6	7
8	9	10	11	12	13	14
15	16	17	18	19	20	21
22	23	24	25	26	27	28
29	30	31	1	2	3	4

Important Dates/Notes

"So! Mr. Carlisle was right! ... I put you on a short leash so you can't harass him anymore, and *look* what you resort to!"

August-September

1711
The British Parliament creates and organizes the first post offices in America.

Notes

September

S	M	T	W	T	F	S
27	28	29	30	31	1	2
3	4	5	6	7	8	9
10	11	12	13	14	15	16
17	18	19	20	21	22	23
24	25	26	27	28	29	30

Monday   28

Summer Bank Holiday (UK-except Scotland)
Tuesday   29

Wednesday   30

Thursday   31

Friday   1

First Day of Spring (Southern Hemisphere)
Saturday   2

Sunday   3

Father's Day (Australia; New Zealand)

The Lone Ranger, long since retired, makes an unpleasant discovery.

September

1755
Dr. Samuel Johnson publishes his *Dictionary of the English Language*, the first comprehensive lexicographical work on English ever undertaken (finally enabling the world to spell "rhythm" and "receive").

Notes

September

S	M	T	W	T	F	S
27	28	29	30	31	1	2
3	4	5	6	7	8	9
10	11	12	13	14	15	16
17	18	19	20	21	22	23
24	25	26	27	28	29	30

Monday 4

Labor Day (USA; Canada)
Tuesday 5

Wednesday 6

Thursday 7

Friday 8

Saturday 9

Sunday 10

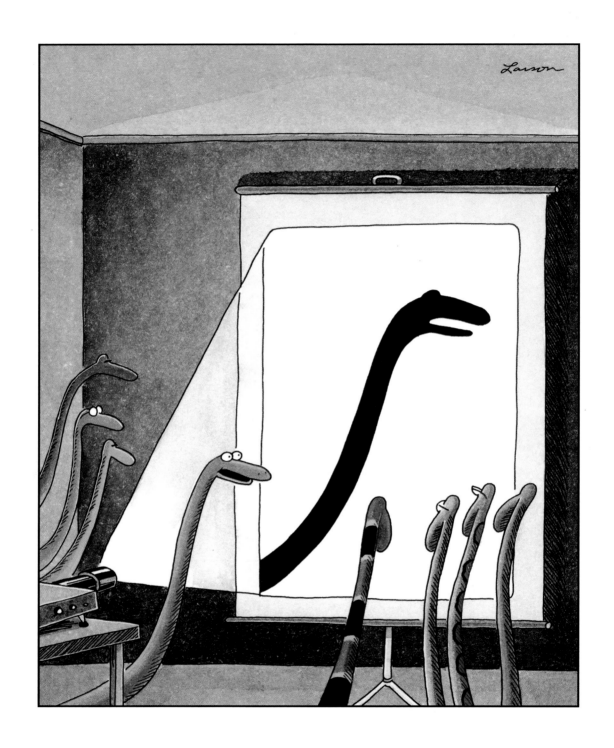

"Now this is ... this is ... well, I guess it's another snake."

September

1759
Étienne de Silhouette is appointed controller general of France. His brief tenure (he serves for a mere nine months) leads people to use his name as a synonym for "shadow."

Notes

September

S	M	T	W	T	F	S
27	28	29	30	31	1	2
3	4	5	6	7	8	9
10	11	12	13	14	15	16
17	18	19	20	21	22	23
24	25	26	27	28	29	30

Monday 11

Tuesday 12

Wednesday 13

Thursday 14

Friday 15

Respect for the Aged Day (Japan)
Saturday 16

Sunday 17

Slowly he would cruise the neighborhood, waiting for that occasional careless child who confused him with another vendor.

September

1777

George Washington has the entire Continental army (at the time 4,000 strong) vaccinated against malaria. It quite possibly saves the army as a fighting force. (The inoculations are known to be painful, which helps explain why George is standing as he crosses the Delaware.)

Notes

September

S	M	T	W	T	F	S
27	28	29	30	31	1	2
3	4	5	6	7	8	9
10	11	12	13	14	15	16
17	18	19	20	21	22	23
24	25	26	27	28	29	30

Monday 18

Tuesday 19

Wednesday 20

Thursday 21

Friday 22

Saturday 23

Autumnal Equinox (Northern Hemisphere)

Sunday 24

October

Sunday	Monday	Tuesday	Wednesday	Thursday	Friday	Saturday
1 Daylight Saving begins (Australia-TAS) National Day (China) Rosh Hashanah	2 Labour Day (Australia-ACT, NSW, SA) Queen's Birthday (Australia-WA)	3 Day of German Unity (German National Day)	4	5	6	7
8	9 Yom Kippur Thanksgiving (Canada) Columbus Day (USA) Sports Day (Japan)	10	11	12	13	14 First Day of Tabernacles
15 Second Day of Tabernacles	16	17	18	19	20	21
22	23 Labour Day (New Zealand) Chulalongkorn Day (Thailand)	24 United Nations Day	25	26	27	28
29	30	31 Halloween	1	2	3	4

September

S	M	T	W	T	F	S
27	28	29	30	31	1	2
3	4	5	6	7	8	9
10	11	12	13	14	15	16
17	18	19	20	21	22	23
24	25	26	27	28	29	30

November

S	M	T	W	T	F	S
29	30	31	1	2	3	4
5	6	7	8	9	10	11
12	13	14	15	16	17	18
19	20	21	22	23	24	25
26	27	28	29	30	1	2

Important Dates/Notes

_____   _____
_____   _____
_____   _____
_____   _____
_____   _____
_____   _____
_____   _____
_____   _____
_____   _____
_____   _____
_____   _____
_____   _____
_____   _____
_____   _____
_____   _____
_____   _____
_____   _____
_____   _____
_____   _____
_____   _____
_____   _____

"Yes ... I believe there's a question in the back."

September-October

1785
Robert Bakewell begins experimenting with the cross-breeding of cows to enhance and create desirable characteristics. (He gets carried away, however, when he begins a quest for "deep, brown eyes—the kind you could just fall into.")

Notes

October

S	M	T	W	T	F	S
1	2	3	4	5	6	7
8	9	10	11	12	13	14
15	16	17	18	19	20	21
22	23	24	25	26	27	28
29	30	31	1	2	3	4

Monday 25

Tuesday 26

Wednesday 27

Thursday 28

Friday 29

St Michael's Day (Canada)

Saturday 30

Rosh Hashanah

Sunday 1

Daylight Saving begins (Australia–TAS)
National Day (China)
Rosh Hashanah

Frog pioneers

October

Notes

October

S	M	T	W	T	F	S
1	2	3	4	5	6	7
8	9	10	11	12	13	14
15	16	17	18	19	20	21
22	23	24	25	26	27	28
29	30	31	1	2	3	4

Monday 2

Labour Day (Australia–ACT, NSW, SA)
Queen's Birthday (Australia–WA)

Tuesday 3

Day of German Unity (German National Day)

Wednesday 4

Thursday 5

Friday 6

Saturday 7

Sunday 8

"You idiot! We want the scent *on* the pillow! On the pillow!"

October

1805

In England, a group called the Thrapthon Association for the Prevention of Felons acquires a bloodhound to help search for poachers and thieves. It is the breed's first recorded use by law enforcement (and replaces the Chihuahua, which—although a good tracker—is prone to being stepped on).

Notes

_____

_____

_____

_____

_____

_____

_____

_____

October

S	M	T	W	T	F	S
1	2	3	4	5	6	7
8	9	10	11	12	13	14
15	16	17	18	19	20	21
22	23	24	25	26	27	28
29	30	31	1	2	3	4

Monday 9
Yom Kippur
Thanksgiving (Canada)
Columbus Day (USA)
Sports Day (Japan)

Tuesday 10

Wednesday 11

Thursday 12

Friday 13

Saturday 14

First Day of Tabernacles
Sunday 15

Second Day of Tabernacles

"OK, crybaby! You want the last soda? Well, let me GET IT READY FOR YOU!"

October

1807
The first carbonated soft drink is created in Philadelphia by Dr. Philip Syng Physick, who uses the fizzy water to treat his patients.

Notes

October

S	M	T	W	T	F	S
1	2	3	4	5	6	7
8	9	10	11	12	13	14
15	16	17	18	19	20	21
22	23	24	25	26	27	28
29	30	31	1	2	3	4

Monday   16

TOM'S B'DAY

Tuesday   17

WENDY'S B'DAY

Wednesday   18

Thursday   19

Friday   20

Saturday   21

Sunday   22

"Any theories on this, Cummings?"

October

Notes

| | Monday | 23 |

Labour Day (New Zealand)
Chulalongkorn Day (Thailand)

| | Tuesday | 24 |

United Nations Day

| | Wednesday | 25 |

| | Thursday | 26 |

| | Friday | 27 |

| | Saturday | 28 |

KEITH'S 20TH

| | Sunday | 29 |

Daylight Saving ends (Canada; USA—except Arizona, Hawaii, Indiana)

October

S	M	T	W	T	F	S
1	2	3	4	5	6	7
8	9	10	11	12	13	14
15	16	17	18	19	20	21
22	23	24	25	26	27	28
29	30	31	1	2	3	4

November

Sunday	Monday	Tuesday	Wednesday	Thursday	Friday	Saturday
29	30	31	1 All Saints Day (Canada; France; Germany)	2 All Souls Day	3 Culture Day (Japan)	4 All Saints Day (Sweden; Finland)
5	6	7 Melbourne Cup Day (Australia -Melbourne only) Election Day (USA)	8	9	10 Veterans' Day observed (USA)	11 Armistice Day Remembrance Day (Canada) Veterans' Day (USA)
12	13	14	15	16	17	18
19	20	21	22	23 Thanksgiving (USA) Labor Thanksgiving Day (Japan)	24	25
26	27	28	29	30 Ramadan begins	1	2

October

S	M	T	W	T	F	S
1	2	3	4	5	6	7
8	9	10	11	12	13	14
15	16	17	18	19	20	21
22	23	24	25	26	27	28
29	30	31	1	2	3	4

December

S	M	T	W	T	F	S
26	27	28	29	30	1	2
3	4	5	6	7	8	9
10	11	12	13	14	15	16
17	18	19	20	21	22	23
24 31	25	26	27	28	29	30

Important Dates/Notes

While their owners sleep, nervous little dogs prepare for their day.

October-November

1821

Caffeine is discovered by Pierre-Joseph Pelletier. It is known to contribute to irritability, depression, diarrhea, insomnia, and other disorders. (I'll take mine black.)

Notes

November

S	M	T	W	T	F	S
29	30	31	1	2	3	4
5	6	7	8	9	10	11
12	13	14	15	16	17	18
19	20	21	22	23	24	25
26	27	28	29	30	1	2

Monday 30

Tuesday 31

Halloween
Wednesday 1

All Saints Day (Canada; France; Germany)
Thursday 2

All Souls Day
Friday 3

Culture Day (Japan)
Saturday 4

All Saints Day (Sweden; Finland)
Sunday 5

Front porch forecasters

November

Notes

November

S	M	T	W	T	F	S
29	30	31	1	2	3	4
5	6	7	8	9	10	11
12	13	14	15	16	17	18
19	20	21	22	23	24	25
26	27	28	29	30	1	2

Monday 6

Tuesday 7

Melbourne Cup Day (Australia-Melbourne only)
Election Day (USA)

Wednesday 8

Thursday 9

Friday 10

Veterans' Day observed (USA)

Saturday 11

Armistice Day
Remembrance Day (Canada)
Veterans' Day (USA)

Sunday 12

"Hey, I'm not crazy. ... Sure, I let him drive once in a while,
but he's never, *never* off this leash for even a second."

November

1905

The U.S. Automobile Association is formed. Its original mission is to provide "scouts" who will warn motorists (all 12 of them) of hidden police traps.

Notes

| Monday | 13 |

| Tuesday | 14 |

| Wednesday | 15 |

| Thursday | 16 |

| Friday | 17 |

| Saturday | 18 |

| Sunday | 19 |

November

S	M	T	W	T	F	S
29	30	31	1	2	3	4
5	6	7	8	9	10	11
12	13	14	15	16	17	18
19	20	21	22	23	24	25
26	27	28	29	30	1	2

"OK, let's see—that's a curse on you, a curse on you, and a curse on you."

November

Notes

Monday	20

Tuesday	21

Wednesday	22

Thursday	23

Thanksgiving (USA)
Labor Thanksgiving Day (Japan)

Friday	24

Saturday	25

Sunday	26

November

S	M	T	W	T	F	S
29	30	31	1	2	3	4
5	6	7	8	9	10	11
12	13	14	15	16	17	18
19	20	21	22	23	24	25
26	27	28	29	30	1	2

December

Sunday	Monday	Tuesday	Wednesday	Thursday	Friday	Saturday
26	27	28	29	30	1 First Day of Summer (Southern Hemisphere)	2
3 First Sunday in Advent	4	5	6 Independence Day (Finland)	7	8	9
10 Constitution Day (Thailand)	11	12	13	14	15	16
17	18	19	20	21	22 Winter Solstice (Northern Hemisphere) First Day of Chanukah	23 Emperor's Birthday (Japan)
24 Christmas Eve 31 New Year's Eve	25 Christmas Day	26 Boxing Day Kwanzaa begins (USA)	27	28	29 Last Day of Chanukah	30

November

S	M	T	W	T	F	S
29	30	31	1	2	3	4
5	6	7	8	9	10	11
12	13	14	15	16	17	18
19	20	21	22	23	24	25
26	27	28	29	30	1	2

January 2001

S	M	T	W	T	F	S
31	1	2	3	4	5	6
7	8	9	10	11	12	13
14	15	16	17	18	19	20
21	22	23	24	25	26	27
28	29	30	31	1	2	3

Important Dates/Notes

"Oh my God, Bernie! You're wearing my nylon?"

November-December

1935

Nylon is developed by DuPont scientist Wallace Hume Carothers. (In stocking form, it flatters women's legs and provides bank robbers with a combination disguise and see-through product.)

WANTED

Notes

Monday 27

Tuesday 28

Wednesday 29

Thursday 30

Ramadan begins

Friday 1

First Day of Summer (Southern Hemisphere)

Saturday 2

Sunday 3

First Sunday in Advent

December

S	M	T	W	T	F	S
26	27	28	29	30	1	2
3	4	5	6	7	8	9
10	11	12	13	14	15	16
17	18	19	20	21	22	23
24 / 31	25	26	27	28	29	30

March 16, 1942: The night before he leaves the Philippines,
Gen. MacArthur works on his farewell address.

December

Notes

December

S	M	T	W	T	F	S
26	27	28	29	30	1	2
3	4	5	6	7	8	9
10	11	12	13	14	15	16
17	18	19	20	21	22	23
24 / 31	25	26	27	28	29	30

Monday 4

Tuesday 5

Wednesday 6

Independence Day (Finland)

Thursday 7

Friday 8

Saturday 9

Sunday 10

Constitution Day (Thailand)

"Take another memo, Miss Wilkens. ... I want to see all reptile personnel in my office first thing tomorrow morning!"

December

1963
Colossus, a 22-foot reticulated python, dies at Highland Park Zoo in Pennsylvania. She was the largest snake held in captivity up to that time. (Her coffin requires 18 pallbearers, also a record.)

Notes

December

S	M	T	W	T	F	S
26	27	28	29	30	1	2
3	4	5	6	7	8	9
10	11	12	13	14	15	16
17	18	19	20	21	22	23
24 31	25	26	27	28	29	30

Monday 11

Tuesday 12

Wednesday 13

Thursday 14

KATIES 2154
Friday 15

Saturday 16

Sunday 17

"Make a note of this, Muldoon. ... The wounds seem to be
caused by bird shot ... big bird shot."

December

1969
Children's Television Workshop premieres *Sesame Street* on PBS.

Notes

December

S	M	T	W	T	F	S
26	27	28	29	30	1	2
3	4	5	6	7	8	9
10	11	12	13	14	15	16
17	18	19	20	21	22	23
24 31	25	26	27	28	29	30

Monday 18

Tuesday 19

Wednesday 20

Thursday 21

Friday 22

Winter Solstice (Northern Hemisphere)
First Day of Chanukah

Saturday 23

VICKY B'DAY   Emperor's Birthday (Japan)

Sunday 24

Christmas Eve

"Hey, you stupid bovines! You'll never get that contraption off the ground! ... Think it'll run on hay? ... Say, maybe you'll make it to the mooooooooon! ..."

December

1981
The first U.S. space shuttle is launched. The astronauts' first dinner on board includes thermostabilized irradiated beefsteak. (Mmmmmm…)

Notes

December

S	M	T	W	T	F	S
26	27	28	29	30	1	2
3	4	5	6	7	8	9
10	11	12	13	14	15	16
17	18	19	20	21	22	23
24 / 31	25	26	27	28	29	30

Monday 25

Christmas Day

Tuesday 26
Boxing Day
Proclamation Day (Australia-SA)
Kwanzaa begins (USA)

Wednesday 27

Thursday 28

Friday 29

Last Day of Chanukah

Saturday 30

Sunday 31

New Year's Eve

January 2001

February

March

April

May

June

July 2001

August

September

October

November

December

January 1999

S	M	T	W	T	F	S
27	28	29	30	31	1	2
3	4	5	6	7	8	9
10	11	12	13	14	15	16
17	18	19	20	21	22	23
24 31	25	26	27	28	29	30

February 1999

S	M	T	W	T	F	S
31	1	2	3	4	5	6
7	8	9	10	11	12	13
14	15	16	17	18	19	20
21	22	23	24	25	26	27
28	1	2	3	4	5	6

March 1999

S	M	T	W	T	F	S
28	1	2	3	4	5	6
7	8	9	10	11	12	13
14	15	16	17	18	19	20
21	22	23	24	25	26	27
28	29	30	31	1	2	3

April 1999

S	M	T	W	T	F	S
28	29	30	31	1	2	3
4	5	6	7	8	9	10
11	12	13	14	15	16	17
18	19	20	21	22	23	24
25	26	27	28	29	30	1

May 1999

S	M	T	W	T	F	S
25	26	27	28	29	30	1
2	3	4	5	6	7	8
9	10	11	12	13	14	15
16	17	18	19	20	21	22
23 30	24 31	25	26	27	28	29

June 1999

S	M	T	W	T	F	S
30	31	1	2	3	4	5
6	7	8	9	10	11	12
13	14	15	16	17	18	19
20	21	22	23	24	25	26
27	28	29	30	1	2	3

July 1999

S	M	T	W	T	F	S
27	28	29	30	1	2	3
4	5	6	7	8	9	10
11	12	13	14	15	16	17
18	19	20	21	22	23	24
25	26	27	28	29	30	31

August 1999

S	M	T	W	T	F	S
1	2	3	4	5	6	7
8	9	10	11	12	13	14
15	16	17	18	19	20	21
22	23	24	25	26	27	28
29	30	31	1	2	3	4

September 1999

S	M	T	W	T	F	S
29	30	31	1	2	3	4
5	6	7	8	9	10	11
12	13	14	15	16	17	18
19	20	21	22	23	24	25
26	27	28	29	30	1	2

October 1999

S	M	T	W	T	F	S
26	27	28	29	30	1	2
3	4	5	6	7	8	9
10	11	12	13	14	15	16
17	18	19	20	21	22	23
24 31	25	26	27	28	29	30

November 1999

S	M	T	W	T	F	S
31	1	2	3	4	5	6
7	8	9	10	11	12	13
14	15	16	17	18	19	20
21	22	23	24	25	26	27
28	29	30	1	2	3	4

December 1999

S	M	T	W	T	F	S
28	29	30	1	2	3	4
5	6	7	8	9	10	11
12	13	14	15	16	17	18
19	20	21	22	23	24	25
26	27	28	29	30	31	1

January 2000

S	M	T	W	T	F	S
26	27	28	29	30	31	1
2	3	4	5	6	7	8
9	10	11	12	13	14	15
16	17	18	19	20	21	22
23 30	24 31	25	26	27	28	29

February 2000

S	M	T	W	T	F	S
30	31	1	2	3	4	5
6	7	8	9	10	11	12
13	14	15	16	17	18	19
20	21	22	23	24	25	26
27	28	29	1	2	3	4

March 2000

S	M	T	W	T	F	S
27	28	29	1	2	3	4
5	6	7	8	9	10	11
12	13	14	15	16	17	18
19	20	21	22	23	24	25
26	27	28	29	30	31	1

April 2000

S	M	T	W	T	F	S
26	27	28	29	30	31	1
2	3	4	5	6	7	8
9	10	11	12	13	14	15
16	17	18	19	20	21	22
23 30	24	25	26	27	28	29

May 2000

S	M	T	W	T	F	S
30	1	2	3	4	5	6
7	8	9	10	11	12	13
14	15	16	17	18	19	20
21	22	23	24	25	26	27
28	29	30	31	1	2	3

June 2000

S	M	T	W	T	F	S
28	29	30	31	1	2	3
4	5	6	7	8	9	10
11	12	13	14	15	16	17
18	19	20	21	22	23	24
25	26	27	28	29	30	1

July 2000

S	M	T	W	T	F	S
25	26	27	28	29	30	1
2	3	4	5	6	7	8
9	10	11	12	13	14	15
16	17	18	19	20	21	22
23 30	24 31	25	26	27	28	29

August 2000

S	M	T	W	T	F	S
30	31	1	2	3	4	5
6	7	8	9	10	11	12
13	14	15	16	17	18	19
20	21	22	23	24	25	26
27	28	29	30	31	1	2

September 2000

S	M	T	W	T	F	S
27	28	29	30	31	1	2
3	4	5	6	7	8	9
10	11	12	13	14	15	16
17	18	19	20	21	22	23
24	25	26	27	28	29	30

October 2000

S	M	T	W	T	F	S
1	2	3	4	5	6	7
8	9	10	11	12	13	14
15	16	17	18	19	20	21
22	23	24	25	26	27	28
29	30	31	1	2	3	4

November 2000

S	M	T	W	T	F	S
29	30	31	1	2	3	4
5	6	7	8	9	10	11
12	13	14	15	16	17	18
19	20	21	22	23	24	25
26	27	28	29	30	1	2

December 2000

S	M	T	W	T	F	S
26	27	28	29	30	1	2
3	4	5	6	7	8	9
10	11	12	13	14	15	16
17	18	19	20	21	22	23
24 31	25	26	27	28	29	30

January 2001

S	M	T	W	T	F	S
31	1	2	3	4	5	6
7	8	9	10	11	12	13
14	15	16	17	18	19	20
21	22	23	24	25	26	27
28	29	30	31	1	2	3

February 2001

S	M	T	W	T	F	S
28	29	30	31	1	2	3
4	5	6	7	8	9	10
11	12	13	14	15	16	17
18	19	20	21	22	23	24
25	26	27	28	1	2	3

March 2001

S	M	T	W	T	F	S
25	26	27	28	1	2	3
4	5	6	7	8	9	10
11	12	13	14	15	16	17
18	19	20	21	22	23	24
25	26	27	28	29	30	31

April 2001

S	M	T	W	T	F	S
1	2	3	4	5	6	7
8	9	10	11	12	13	14
15	16	17	18	19	20	21
22	23	24	25	26	27	28
29	30	1	2	3	4	5

May 2001

S	M	T	W	T	F	S
29	30	1	2	3	4	5
6	7	8	9	10	11	12
13	14	15	16	17	18	19
20	21	22	23	24	25	26
27	28	29	30	31	1	2

June 2001

S	M	T	W	T	F	S
27	28	29	30	31	1	2
3	4	5	6	7	8	9
10	11	12	13	14	15	16
17	18	19	20	21	22	23
24	25	26	27	28	29	30

July 2001

S	M	T	W	T	F	S
1	2	3	4	5	6	7
8	9	10	11	12	13	14
15	16	17	18	19	20	21
22	23	24	25	26	27	28
29	30	31	1	2	3	4

August 2001

S	M	T	W	T	F	S
29	30	31	1	2	3	4
5	6	7	8	9	10	11
12	13	14	15	16	17	18
19	20	21	22	23	24	25
26	27	28	29	30	31	1

September 2001

S	M	T	W	T	F	S
26	27	28	29	30	31	1
2	3	4	5	6	7	8
9	10	11	12	13	14	15
16	17	18	19	20	21	22
23 30	24	25	26	27	28	29

October 2001

S	M	T	W	T	F	S
30	1	2	3	4	5	6
7	8	9	10	11	12	13
14	15	16	17	18	19	20
21	22	23	24	25	26	27
28	29	30	31	1	2	3

November 2001

S	M	T	W	T	F	S
28	29	30	31	1	2	3
4	5	6	7	8	9	10
11	12	13	14	15	16	17
18	19	20	21	22	23	24
25	26	27	28	29	30	1

December 2001

S	M	T	W	T	F	S
25	26	27	28	29	30	1
2	3	4	5	6	7	8
9	10	11	12	13	14	15
16	17	18	19	20	21	22
23 30	24 31	25	26	27	28	29